Henry Rogers
Illustrations by Victoria Yakesch

Maddox Bonn Media, LLC Texas

Thank you for buying an authorized edition of this book and for complying with copyright laws by not reproducing, scanning, or distributing any part of it in any form without permission. You are supporting independent authors, illustrators and creators and allowing us to continue publishing books for every reader.

Visit us online at antiwokebaby.org

Copyright © 2023 Henry Rogers

"Dedicated to the truth-seekers, free thinkers, and torchbearers of hard-won rights all"

Anti-Woke Baby seeks what is real with sincerity and grace.

He knows the West is an idea more than any one place.

Anti-Woke Baby knows our shared history, culture, and worldview have brought more health, wealth and freedom to humanity than all other ways of life.

She knows this is a truth that's worth protecting, promoting, and valuing to save humanity from unnecessary strife.

2. See the Individual

We're all different colors, shapes, and sizes, it's clear as day to see. But if I really want to know who you are as a person, using just your words and actions is the key.

3. Be Responsible for Your Own Thoughts

Don't blindly follow what others say, or accept ideas without checking. Disagreeing should be welcomed in a sincere and open setting.

4. Know Your History

Educate yourself about the West and its grand traditions.

Make sure sharing those facts is one of your life's key missions.

6. Take Action to Stay Free

Claim your rights, they start with freedom of speech.

That means to think and speak at will, no thoughts or words are out of reach.

7. Celebrate and Give Thanks

Don't be ashamed of the greatness of the West, and the dreams it has fulfilled.

Cheer on freedom's march, and give thanks though it stumbles, it still marches uphill.

8. Be Humble in All That You Do

You're anti-woke, not anti-human, the well-being of people comes first; you want to see them grow. Helping others helps you too, and together, we discover there is always more to know.

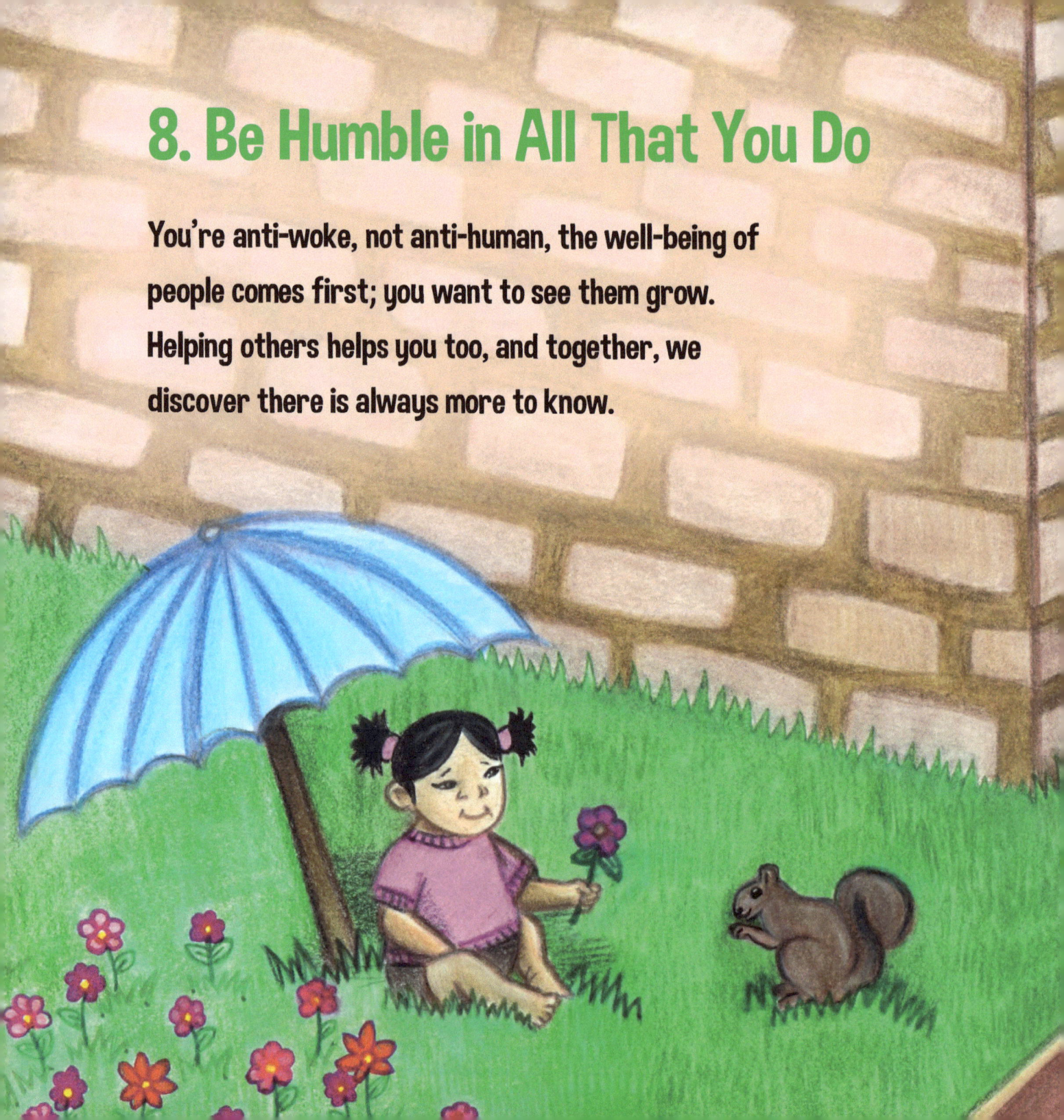

9. Have Faith That Goodness Will Win

Fight the good fight, defend what's right, and keep the laws just and fair. Do your part and together we'll spread freedom and truth everywhere.

The End

Continue the conversation at

antiwokebaby.org

What is woke? ↗